LITTLE BITS OF WISDOM

LITTLE BITS OF WISDOM

Edited by Dean Walley

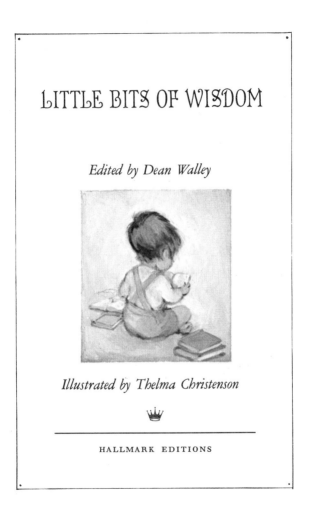

Illustrated by Thelma Christenson

HALLMARK EDITIONS

LITTLE BITS OF WISDOM

One, two,
whatever you do,
Start it well
and carry it through.

Patience is a virtue,
Virtue is a grace;
Both put together
Make a very pretty face.

Say well and do well
End with one letter;
Say well is good,
Do well is better.

Little strokes
Fell great oaks.

No one is too small
to be able
to help a friend.

Quarrels never
could last long,
If on one side only
lay the wrong.

Of a little take a little,
You're kindly
welcome, too;
Of a little leave a little,
'Tis manners so to do.

Anger in its time
and place
May assume
a kind of grace,
If it has some
reason in it
And never lasts
beyond a minute.

When you wish
for something new,
Believe it's on
its way to you;
And when the time
is right, you'll find
You'll have just what
you had in mind!

What you would
seem to be, be really.

Little drops of water,
Little grains of sand,
Make the mighty ocean
And the pleasant land.
Little deeds of kindness,
Little words of love,
Help to make
earth happy
Like the heaven above.

Of all the sayings
in the world
The one to see
you through
Is never trouble trouble
Till trouble troubles you.

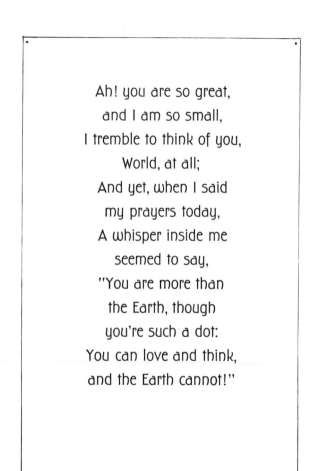

Ah! you are so great,
and I am so small,
I tremble to think of you,
World, at all;
And yet, when I said
my prayers today,
A whisper inside me
seemed to say,
"You are more than
the Earth, though
you're such a dot:
You can love and think,
and the Earth cannot!"

Nothing dries sooner
than a tear.

Who has seen
the wind?
Neither you nor I:
But when the trees
bow down their heads,
The wind is passing by.

Penny and penny
Laid up will be many.
Who will not
save a penny
Shall never have many.

He that would live
in peace and at ease,
Must not speak all
he knows,
nor judge all he sees.

Wilful waste makes
woeful want,
And I may live to say,
Oh! how I wish
I had the bread
That once
I threw away!

So many gentle
friends are near
Whom one can
Scarcely see,
I should never
feel alone
Wherever I may be.

Hide not your talents;
for use they were made!
What's a sundial
in the shade?

He prayeth best,
who loveth best
All things both
great and small;
For the dear God
who loveth us,
He made
and loveth all.